Tree-
HOUSE
Comix
Proudly
Presents

CAT KID
COMIC CLUB
COLLABORATIONS

WORDS, ILLUSTRATIONS, AND ARTWORK BY
DAV PILKEY

WITH DIGITAL COLOR BY JOSE GARIBALDI

SCHOLASTIC

Published in the UK by Scholastic, 2023
1 London Bridge, London, SE1 9BG
Scholastic Ireland, 89E Lagan Road, Dublin
Industrial Estate, Glasnevin, Dublin, D11 HP5F

First published in the US by Scholastic Inc, 2022
Text and illustrations © Dav Pilkey, 2022

ISBN 978 0702 32658 5

A CIP catalogue record for this book is available
from the British Library.

Printed in China
Paper made from wood grown in sustainable forests
and other controlled sources.

1 3 5 7 9 10 8 6 4 2

www.scholastic.co.uk

Illustrations, 3-D models, photography and hand lettering by Dav Pilkey.
All mini comics colored by Dav Pilkey using pencils, markers, pastels,
ink, crayons, and colored pencils. 3-D models built out of recycled
cardboard, putty, wood, wire, plasticine, tape, glue, broken toys, candy,
graham crackers, frosting, gum, polyester batting, Styrofoam, and
other repurposed items.

Digital color by Jose Garibaldi | Flatting by Aaron Polk
Editor: Ken Geist | Editorial Team: Megan Peace and Jonah Newman
Book design by Dav Pilkey and Phil Falco
Creative Director: Phil Falco

CHAPTERS & COMICS

To Cece Bell, Tom Angleberger,
Oscar, and Charlie

CHAPTER 1
OFF TO A BAD START

Hello, and welcome back to **ANOther DRAMATIC DAY...**

...of the CAT KID COMIC CLUB!

I'm your host, SARAH HATOFF, and today, **TWENTY-ONE BABY FROGS...**

...Will DIVE into CREATIVITY!

This is Li'l Petey and Molly.

They're the President and Vice President of this **THRILLING** club!

Tell me...

... are you **EXCITED** About Yesterday's ENCHANTING, EXPLOSIVE, ELECTRIFYING NEWS????

Yeah.

Yeah.

Okay, **CUT!**

Remember how we talked about those **ONE-WORD Answers?**

Yeah. Yeah.

So let's start again...

... and let's all try to be **SUPER ENTHUSIASTIC!**

Okay.

Okay.

Friday interview, take twelve.

We're back with Li'l Petey and Molly.

So— Yesterday's news was **VERY EXCITING,** wasn't it?

Yes, ma'am.

Yes, ma'am.

Well why don't you **TELL US ABOUT iT???**

Umm... Okay.

These four kids in our club...

... are going to Get their Comic **PUBLiShed!!!**

It's Gonna be a **REAL BooK** and stuff.

FLippY is the father of all 21 students.

And Me!!!

Oh, Yes. He's Molly's Dad, too.

What's up, FLippY?

UNFortuNateLY, there will be NO COMIC CLUB TODAY!

WHY NOT?

BECAUSE YOUR BEDROOM IS A MESS!!!!

Can I clean it up **LATER**?

NO!!!

NOW GET GOING!

AW, MAAAAN!!!

I NEVER GET TO DO ANYTHING!

WHAT DID YOU SAY?

I said, "Okay, Daddy. I'll go clean up my room."

NO FAIR!!!

How come we **ALL** Got **Punished**...

...Just because **MOLLY** didn't clean **her** room?

BUT, DADDY!!!

It's Not FAIR!!!

We CLEANED OUR ROOMS!!!

Me too!

AND we FINISHED our COMICS!!!

But now we don't Get to **SHARE Them!**

It's the WORST DAY of ALL Time!

Well...

...if You want...

...You can Share Your comics with our **TV Audience!!!**

WE CAN READ OUR COMICS on TV?

Yes. FOR the **WHOLE WORLD!!!**

Chapter 2

The Best Day of All Time

Today's First comic is by Wendy and Raine...

...Who are working **TOGETHER**...

...On a serialized **BIOGRAPHY**...

...about their **DAD** when he was a kid!

I adapted the story...

... and I drew the Pictures on my computer!

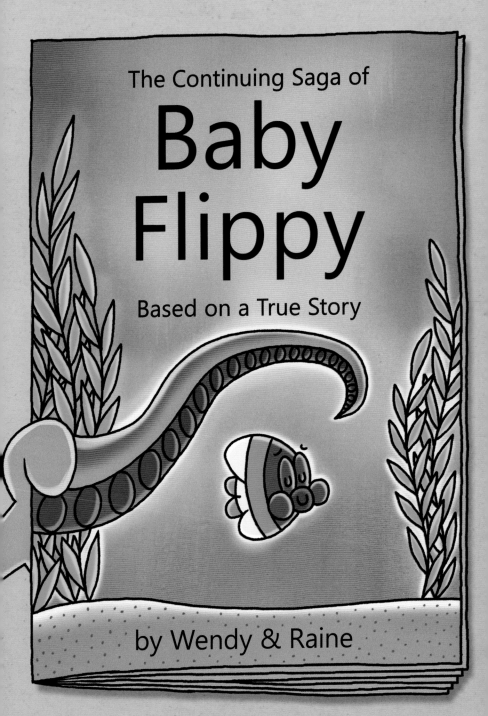

The Continuing Saga of

Baby Flippy

Based on a True Story

by Wendy & Raine

When we last saw our hero...

...he was in BIG TROUBLE!!!

He had been CAPTURED by KIDNAPPERS...

...BULLIED by a BLOCKHEAD...

...SLAMMED by a SHIPWRECK...

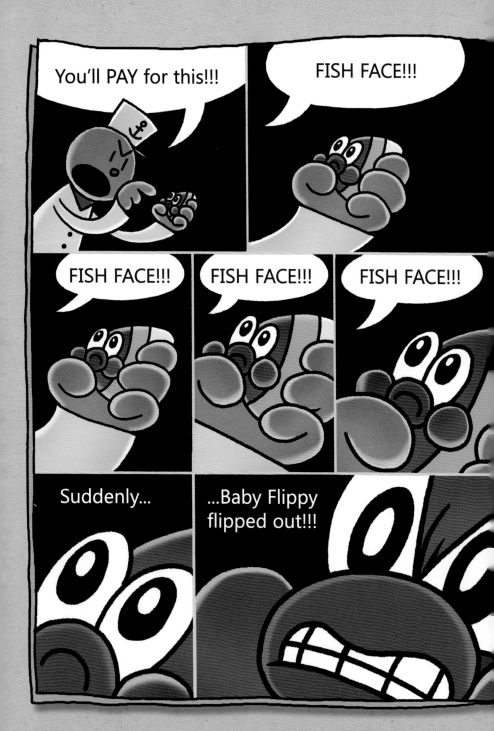

He started to grow...

...and grow...

...and grow...

...and GROW!!!

OH, NO! The gamma rays in that lightning bolt...

...must have SUPA CHARGED his DNA...

...causing him to TRANSFORM into a TERRIFYING BABY...

...and to grow a pair of purple pants for some reason.

BABY ANGRY!!!

Uh-oh!!!

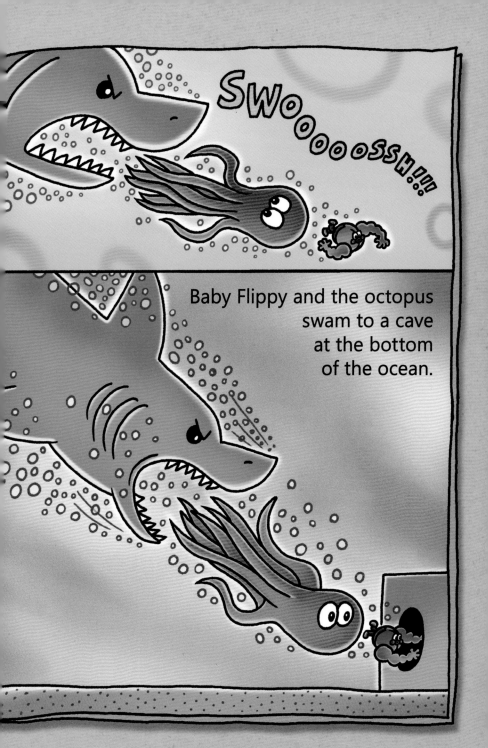

Baby Flippy and the octopus
swam to a cave
at the bottom
of the ocean.

That shark can't fit inside this cave...

...so let's wait here until it leaves.

Try to relax.

Be more chill...

Be more chill...

Be more chill...

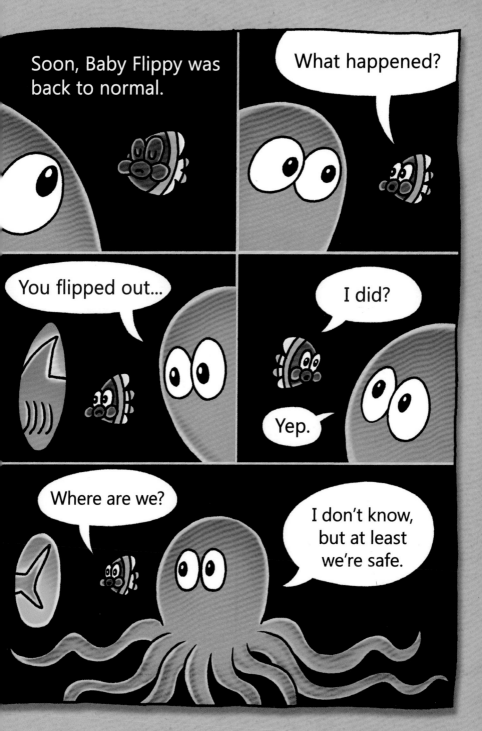

We know. But your **TRUE STORY** was kind of boring.

Yeah.

Girls...

...Just because you **think** something...

...doesn't mean you need to **SAY** **it** **OUT** **LOUD**!!!!!

Your words can be hurtful.

We're sorry, Daddy.

Okay.

Hey, Daddy, when you went to space, how did—

I NEVER WENT TO SPACE!!!

NOW GET BACK IN THERE AND CLEAN UP THOSE BEDROOMS!!!

IN THE
AUTUMN
POND

HAIKU
SHODO
PHOTOS

AND
BY

SUMMER
AND
STARLA

反
響
音

in the autumn pond
every leaf casts a shadow
each sound, an echo

38

見
性

the sun shows the way
but the sun is not the way
there's a difference

autumn days grow cold
yet in that winding downward
promises appear

乱舞

each star shines brightly
sparkling crisp on frigid twigs

dancing in breezes

tiny scarlet leaf

clinging fiercely
to the branch

無

it's time to let go

little fallen leaves
your journey is not over

now you are a path

Each Shodo character can have many meanings.
These are some of the meanings for the ones we painted.

 = "han" – One meaning is "to return."

 = "kyou" – Sound or reverberate.
    Together, "hankyou" means "echo."

見 = "ken" – Seeing.

性 = "sho" – Nature, essense.
    Together, "kensho" means
      "to see one's nature from within."

休 = "yasumu" – To rest.

乱 = "ran" – Disorder.

舞 = "bu" – Dance.
    Together, "ranbu" means
      "boisterous dance."

無 = "mu" – Nothing. In this case,
    it means "although we may lose
    everything, new opportunities arise."

旅 = "tabi" – Journey.

Nao'omi Kuratani, Akemi Kobayashi, Shunsuke Okunishi,
A New Dictionary of Kanji Usage (Tokyo; Gakken Co., LTD., 1982).

Summer and Starla would like to
acknowledge and thank the artists who
continue to inspire them, including:

Shoko Kanazawa, who is one of Japan's
most highly respected Shodo artists. She
paints from her heart with giant brushes.
She also has Down's Syndrome.

And

Shozo Sato, author of *Shodo: The Quiet Art
of Japanese Zen Calligraphy* (Rutland:
Tuttle Publishing, 2014).

45

While the kids clean their rooms...

...Summer and Starla have allowed us to taG alonG...

...as we diG deeper into their creative Process.

click

How do You Get inspired to make Your Haiku Photo comics?

Well...

I never show anyone my **BAD** pictures...

...I only show the **GOOD** ones.

Oh.

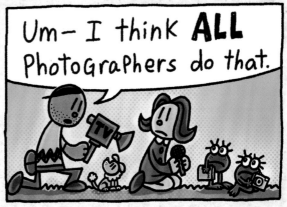

Um— I think **ALL** photographers do that.

They do?

Yeah. That's what **I** do...

...and **I'm** a **PRO!!!**

REALLY?

WOW! I'm just like a **PRO!!!**

Starla, can you teach us how to write a **HAIKU?**

click click
click
click click

Sure! They're just short descriptions of **NATURE**...

Each poem has **THREE LINES**...

...and each line has **BEATS** — just like **MUSIC!**

BEAT

CHAPTER 4

Gilbert and Curly Heed the Call

45 Minutes Later...

ALRiGht, kids— I've checked everybody's rooms...

...and **MOST** of You have done a Pretty Good Job.

You're all excused untiL suppertime...

...All except for Curly and Gilbert!

HOORAY!!!

...and **Grow** and **Grow!**

Hey, Daddy!

Are those Guys done Yet?

The Comic Club is having A **BiG MEETiNG!**

We're making a new Comic, Molly!

It's called **FroGZiLLA!**

I bet You'll never Guess what it's About!!!

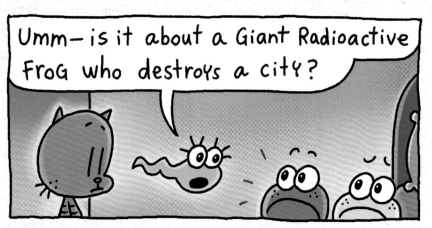

69

A **PARODY** is a **HUMOROUS VERSION** of somebody else's idea!

Oh.

Are you saying we can't **COPY** Godzilla...

...but we can **MAKE FUN** of Godzilla?

Yep. That's totally LeGal!!!

Let's MAKE A PARODY!!!

CHAPTER 5

The PARODY

THAT ReLied HeaviLY ON The FAiR-Use DeFense To FoResTaLL AnY LiaBiLiTY FoR COPYRIGHT InFrinGeMenT

Well folks, the sun has set...

...and today's drama has slipped peacefully away.

YOU KIDS GET BACK IN THOSE BEDS RIGHT NOW!

HA HA HA HA HA HA

And now it's SATURDAY!!!

A day of **HOPE** and **GRACEFUL NEW beginnings!**

YOU KIDS GET OUT OF THOSE BEDS RIGHT NOW!!!!!

The comic club doesn't meet on the weekends...

...Yet **ALL** of these kids...

...Continue to be creative!!!

After a hearty breakfast...

We're almost done.

Gilbert's just coloring the last two pages.

While we wait, I need to ask:

What's that sign all about?

FAIL MISRABLY

Oh. That's to remind us.

To remind you to FAIL???

Oh.

You misspelled "miserably."

FAIL MISRABLY

Yeah, we know.

Okay! The color is all finished!

Now we put the pages in order...

...Staple them...

KACHUNK

KA CHUNK

KACHUNK

...And it's Ready to DEVOUR!!!

80

83

WILL Felix and Jax save the world?

CAN they rescue Dog Man and Chief?

... And **WHEN** will they **EVER** reach Level 9 ???

pew pew pew

Find out in our next thrilling Parody...

FROGZILLA VS. MECHAFROGZILLA

WOW! That was AWESOME!!!

Thanks!

I can't believe you made this in ONE DAY!

Well, it was a lot of work!

Yeah. When we started writing...

...our story wasn't very good.

So we RE-WROTE it TWO TIMES!

And each time it got better...

...and better!

CHAPTER 6

Business Partners

104

CHAPTER 7
Melvin and Naomi Get Their Chance

Meanwhile...

CRAFT ROOM

FAiL MisRabl

We're back with the **HACKER BROTHERS!**

So tell me...

...How did You make all of these **COOL TOYS?**

Um— well...

...they all started off as **BROKEN TOYS...**

... and we **HACKED** 'em!

Yeah. Like, we took this baby doll head...

... and stuck it on this wrestler guy's body...

... and made an **ALL-NEW GUY!**

How did You Get his new head to stay on?

We used wire and hot GLue!!!

We use lots of Duck tape, too.

I think it's called **"DUCT"** tape.

Yeah, we know.

But it's **FUNNER** to say "Duck tape."

While we hack our toys...

...We talk about story ideas...

Then we write down our ideas...

... and make a **SKETCH COMIC.**

Some People call these **ROUGH DRAFTS!**

But **WE** call 'em **STORYBOARDS!**

Then we set up our toys...

...and take Pictures!!!

click

We try to make the Photos look like the storyboards!

Then we Put it all toGether on the computer!

Let's take a Look!!!

CHUBBS McSPIDERBUTT
easy... ★★★
SPIDER

written and directed by
the hacker BROS

In our last adventure...

...The Not Very Nice Club...

...was not feeling very nice.

It's All **Your** fault, Scott!!!

FiRST, You knocked BiG Bubba's head off...

...Then You FLATTENED IT...

...**Then** You went to the **STORE**...

...and bought him a **BABY HEAD**...

... as a **REPLACEMENT!**

Now we have to call him **BIG BUBBA BABYHEAD!!!!!**

HEY! Don't call me that!!!

WHY?

It's not very nice!!!

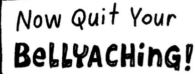

...I'd be stuck looking like this **FOREVER!!!**

Thank Goodness **THAT** will never happen!!!

click

VRRRRRRRR

KA·CHONK

FWOOOOSH

SSSSSHH

Meanwhile...

I think I'll close early.

SSSSSHH

SLAM

♫ La La La La! ♫

Meanwhile...

Here's Your tooty-fruity vanilla kiwi froyo Soda, Jake.

Do You want sprinkles?

No.

What's WRONG, Little buddy?

I think we're too **SOFT,** Chubbs.

Really? Yeah. I mean..

...Do you think **BATMAN** drinks stuff like this?

No.

Do you think **SUPERMAN** lives in a **CUSTOMIZED VAN...**

...with a **Built-in Disco?** I don't think so.

Do You think Spider-Man has heated toilet seats and flashy neon signs???

Probably not.

If we want to be **FAMOUS** like those Guys...

...and have **OUR PICTURES** on Kids' Pajamas...

...then we need to **BE HARD!!!**

All we've done **LATELY** is eat **SUSHI**...

... and play **ViDEO GAMES !!!**

BEEP BEEP BEEP BEEP BEEP

Oh, **NO!** It's the **SPIDER COMPUTER!**

Come on, Chubbs!!!

Spider Computer

STORE GOT BLOWED UP

Now's our chance!!!

Okay...

...but Jake?

Yes, Chubbs?

Weren't Batman's Mom and Dad killed brutally...

...when he was just a little kid?

Yep...

...right in front of him.

And didn't Spider-Man's Uncle Get **STABBED** to death?

Sho<u>t</u> to death. But Yeah.

And didn't Superman's Parents **EXPLODE**???

They Sure did...

...along with 1.4 billion **OTHER** innocent folks.

Meanwhile...

You BLEW UP The WHOLE STORE!!!

Nice GoinG, Scott! Sowwy!

All of my HOPES and DREAMS...

...have been REDUCED to ASHES!!!

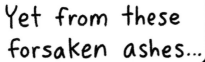

Yet from these forsaken ashes...

Rub Rub Rub

Rub Rub

Rub Rub Rub

A **MiGHTY** Phoenix has risen!!!

From now on, Ye shall call me:

"THE MIGHTY Phoenix!"

Nah. We like **BiG Bubba Babyhead** better!!!

I TOLD YOU NOT TO CALL ME THAT!

It's NOT VERY Nice!!!

Will the **Not Very Nice Club EVER** win?

Will our heroes **EVER** be violent enough to appear on Kids' pajamas?

And **Will** Scott **EVER** Learn to Read???

FIND OUT in the next Epic Adventure of **CHUBBS McSPIDERBUTT** COMING SOON

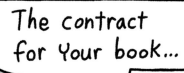

140

Wait — they Paid us **BEFORE** we finished the book?

Yes. It's called an **ADVANCE.**

Now, **MOST** of the money is going into the **COLLEGE FUND**...

Aw, Maaan!

...but if you kids are **SERIOUS** about working **TOGETHER** on this book...

...then I think it's only fair...

144

WHAT is THE PROBLEM?

Well, we think we should GET **MORE MONEY**...

...'CUZ WE'VE GOT **MORE RESPONSIBILITY!**

OR, at least we **TRY**...

... but you never **LET US!!!**

CHAPTER 8

The Smallest Act of Kindness

Okay, kids. While Naomi and Melvin Run an errand...

...I wanted to talk with You all...

...about **GIVING** Some of Your new fortune...

...to help others in need.

Like who?

Well, there's a shelter over in Bedford Falls...

... and they help **LOTS** of people and animals in our community.

They Give food, warm beds...

... and toys and books to anyone who needs them.

...and toys and books.

Poppy, I think you should keep this.

Fifty dollars is not going to make **THAT** much of a difference.

Here, Daddy.

Now it's a **Hundred!**

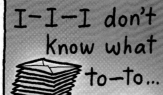

...Two Large French **Flies**...

...and a Supa-Sized **SNAKE!**

WELP, the CUSTOMER is always RIGHT!

and so...

Boop
Beep
Boop
Beee
Beep
Boop

HELLo, France?

Wee-wee?

P.S. "Wee-Wee" means "Yes, Yes" in French.

164

165

169

174

175

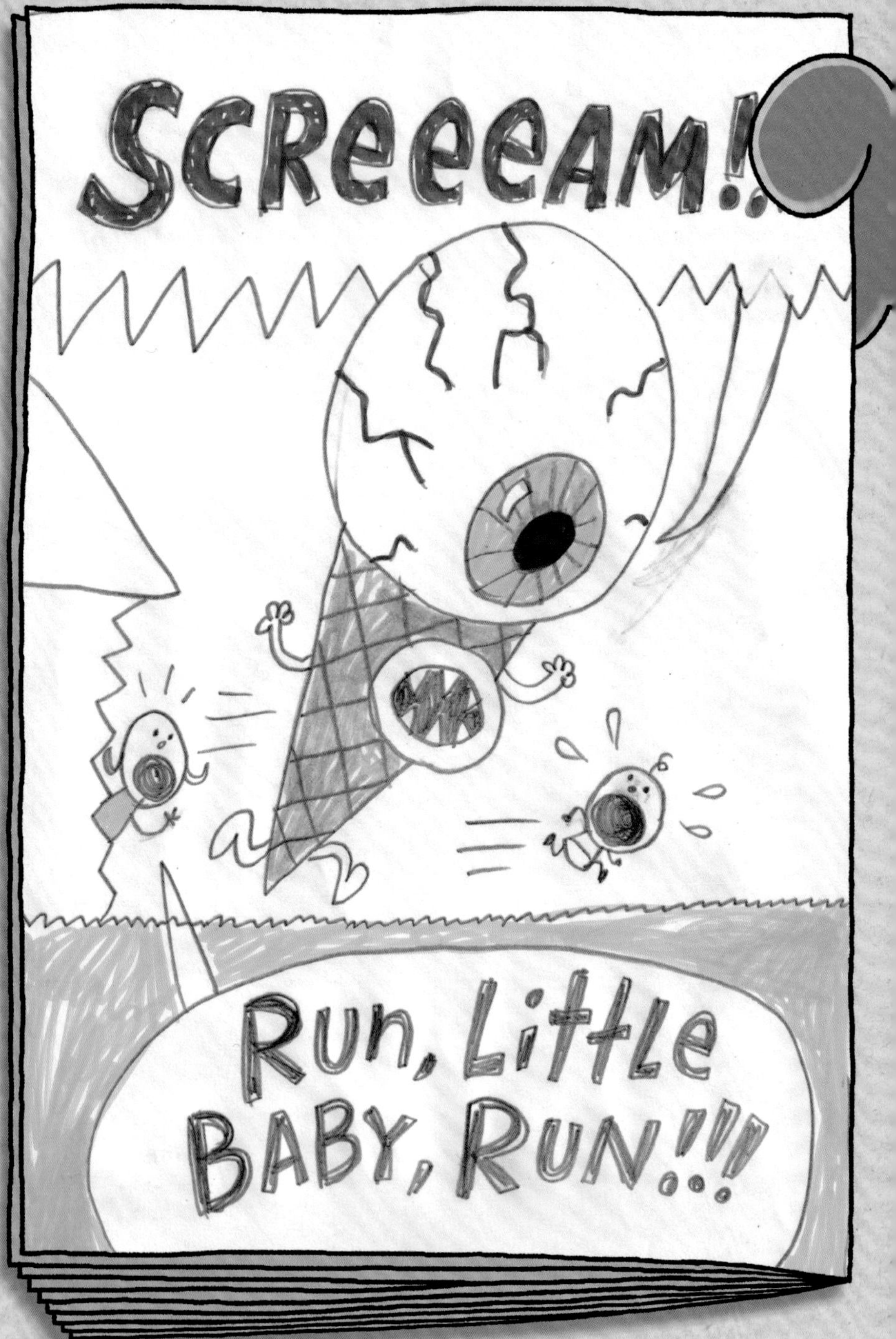
SCREEEAM!!
Run, Little BABY, RUN!!!

Later... **PHIL'S ELECTRONICS**

Phone Screen Repair $75.00 ALL MAKES AND MODELS

Thanks, Mister Falcon!!!

Daddy's Phone is Almost like **NEW!**

And **WE'RE** Almost out of **MONEY!**

But I'm not Leaving **EMPTY-HANDED!**

Where are You Going?

CHAPTER 9

REGRETS

And finally, folks...

...EL and their brothers Corky and Pink...

...have created a **NEW** comic...

... by photographing cookies and candy!

We used frosting and gum to stick it all together!!!

Sweeeeet!!!

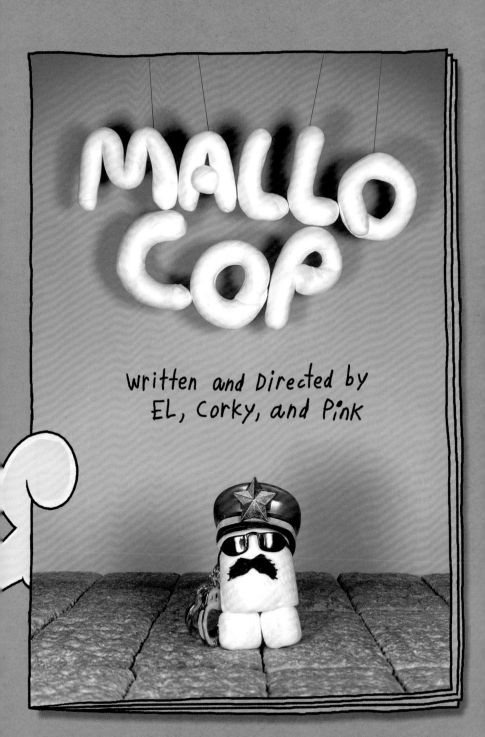

One time a marshmallow...

...wanted to be a cop.

...So he paid a visit...

COPS

...to Chief Candi D. Spencer.

What makes you think **YOU** can be a cop?

I've Got these SunGlasses.

Unfortunately...

...the only car we have now...

...is this old clunker.

We call her "Gramma."

Gramma Crackers!!!

She's mostly Graham crackers!

Hmm— Chocolate, marshmallow, and Graham Crackers?

Something tells me that **we**...

...will Go very nicely toGether!!!

We won't let You down, Chief!!!!!

And so...

Story + Art by EL
Art + Photographs by Corky
Art + Digital Wizardry by Pink

Yeah! I ate Gramma Crackers all by myself!!!

I ate the Chief's desk!!!

And I ate everybody else!!!

Then we ate the fire and the floors...

... and the cotton candy smoke...

Is that why you three had tummy aches last night?

195

201

I'M **NEVER** GONNA FIGURE OUT MY PURPOSE!!!

Your PURPOSE?

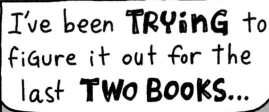

I've been **TRYING** to figure it out for the last **TWO BOOKS...**

...but it's Just **TOO HARD!!!**

Really? Mine was **EASY!**

Those are Just little things, Poppy.

How do **THEY** make the **WHoLe WorLd** a better place?

Wow!

That's a Pretty Good Purpose, Poppy!

Thanks.

You can borrow it if You want to...

...at least until You figure out Your own.

CHAPTER 10

NAOMI AND MELVIN LEARN THEIR LESSON (SORT OF)

Soon...

So let me get this straight:

AFTER you fixed my phone...

...you spent the rest of your money...

...on CHOCOLATE-COVERED GUMMY WORMS???

Yeah.

It was her idea.

And now you both have tummy aches?

Yeah.

Yeah.

216

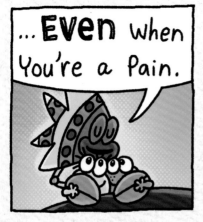

...Another day of GRIPPING DRAMA has ended!

WILL the Creativity CONTINUE???

WILL the DRAMA DECREASE?

And WILL Naomi and Melvin EVER Straighten up and FLY Right???

FIND OUT in OUR NEXT DRAMATIC SAGA!

CAT KID COMIC CLUB

BOOK 5 is COMING Soon!

NOTES & FUN FACTS

☆ The theme of this book (small things can have great effects) was inspired by the following quote: "Behold also the ships, which though they be so great, and are driven of fierce winds, yet are they turned about with a very small helm..." – James 3:4 (KJV)

☆ Poppy's purpose (pages 206-211) is based on a scientific ideology and branch of mathematics known as "chaos theory." This concept proposes that things that appear random and insignificant actually display underlying patterns and interconnectedness, which can have a profound effect on other seemingly independent things.

☆ Quinquagintaquadringentilliard (page 222) is a real number equal to 10^{2703}, or 1 with 2,703 zeros after it. It would take about two pages to write the entire number.

☆ Googolplex is also a real number, equal to $10^{10^{100}}$, or a 1 with so many zeros after it, it would be impossible to write. If you could, the number of pages you'd need would fill up enough books to overflow the observable universe.

☆ The number "googolplex" was coined in 1920 by a nine-year-old named Milton Sirotta, who described the number as "one, followed by writing zeros until you get tired." Milton's uncle, mathematician Edward Kasner, adapted this number to the standardized $10^{10^{100}}$.

☆ The video game cabinets in EASY SPIDER were made (hacked) from toys that actually work. Each game still works and can be played—although the games are different than what is shown.

☆ All the smoke in EASY SPIDER was made out of polyester stuffing (from an old pillow) glued to recycled paper.

☆ The campfire in MALLO COP was made from strips of dried mango "toothpicked" to wheat gluten "logs." The smoke was cotton candy.

☆ "Wee-wee" really does mean "yes, yes" (or "yeah, yeah") in French. It's spelled "oui, oui," but it's pronounced "wee-wee."